Dear Parents,

Thank you for purchasing our book. We are thrilled to be part of your child's reading journey. By choosing this book, you have taken an important first step in improving your child's reading skills.

To make the most out of this book, we recommend reading one to two stories a day for about thirty minutes. Feel free to break this session into two parts if needed to keep your child engaged and focused. After reading, encourage your child to color the picture that accompanies each story. This not only makes learning fun but also reinforces what they have just read.

We understand that starting a new reading program can feel overwhelming, but remember that consistency is key. Setting aside dedicated reading time each day will help build a strong routine and foster a love for reading in your child. If you're unsure where to start, focusing on vowel sounds in order we have provided is a great approach. This foundational skill is crucial for developing strong reading abilities and will give your child the confidence they need to progress.

Additionally, creating a comfortable and distraction-free reading environment can make a significant difference. Choose a quiet spot where your child can concentrate, and make sure they have all the materials they need, including crayons for coloring. Positive reinforcement and praise can also motivate your child and make the learning experience enjoyable.

Should you need any guidance or a FREE placement test, please don't hesitate to reach out. We are here to support you and your child every step of the way. Our goal is to provide you with the tools and resources necessary to make reading a positive and rewarding experience.

Thank you once again for your support. Together, we can make a significant difference in your child's reading journey. Your commitment and involvement play a crucial role in their success, and we are honored to be a part of this important milestone.

Warm regards,
Budding Brains Books

TABLE OF CONTENTS

Short Vowel A

Sam had a cat. The cat sat on a mat. The mat was flat. Sam's cat ran to a fat rat. The rat had a hat. The hat was on a bat. The bat sat with the rat and the cat on the mat. Sam and his dad clapped. Sam was glad.

Pam has a fat ball. Pam taps the fat ball. It can go fast. Pam ran and bats the ball. Pam can pass the ball and land it on sand. It is a fad. Pam can tag the ball.

Pat has a pet rat. The rat can nap and tap. Pat and the rat sat on a mat. The rat ran at a bat. Pat had a hat. The rat sat in the hat. They had a jam. Pat can pat the rat. The rat is fat. Pat and the rat had fun. They ran in the sun.

Sam, a fat cat, sat on a mat. A bat and a rat ran past Sam. The bat had a hat. The rat had a tag. Sam saw the bat and the rat. Sam ran at the rat and the bat. The rat ran to a van. The bat sat on a can. Sam sat back on the mat.

Ann had a pan. In the pan was jam. Ann sat and had jam. Jam was Ann's fad. Ann had jam on a mat. Ann had jam and ran. Jam was all Ann had. Ann had a nap. Jam was Ann's top snack. Ann had a map. The map had a tag. The tag had a tab. Ann was glad.

An ant had a map. The ant ran past a bag and a mat. The mat was on a tan van. The ant had to tap a pan to pass. It was not a sad day. The ant had a jam and sat on a pad. The map had a tag. The ant was glad. The end.

Nat is a fat lad fish. Nat has a cap. Nat can zap to the cab. He can dash and zap fast. Nat is sad in a bag. He can nap in a van. Nat is mad at a cat. He can tap on the glass. Nat had a jam.

Short Vowel O

Tom has a dog. The dog's tag has mom and pop on it. The dog can hop and jog. Tom and the dog go to a log to sit. Tom has a hot rod. The dog hops in. They go to a pond. The dog got a lot of mud on him. Tom got him in a tub to mop him off. The dog is not hot now.

Rox got a doll from Mom. Rox and the doll hop on logs. They jog to a pond. The doll drops in mud! Rox sobs. Mom jogs to Rox. Mom pats Rox on the back. Mom and Rox wash the doll. Rox is glad. Rox and the doll nap on a cot.

Tom got a top. The top can hop and zap. Tom has a dog, Ron. Ron and the top had fun. Ron ran and the top spun. Tom claps and stops. The top hops. Tom and Ron play. The dog is hot. It is fun to hop and pop. Tom's top is the best.

A fox jogs on logs. He hops on top of a box. The box is not so hot, but it is not so cold. The fox sips on a pot of hot rot. He nods and naps. A dog trots by. The fox hops up and dots off. The dog yaps, but the fox is not on top of the box.

An ox got on a log. The log was on top of a bog. The ox did not jog. It sat and had a nod. The fog got so big, it hid the log. A dog ran up. It got on the log too. The ox and the dog sat in the fog on the log.

Tom, the cop, got on top of a log to hop. A fox got his hot pot. "Stop!" Tom yells to the fox. The fox drops the pot and jogs off. Tom hops off the log and jogs to the pot. It is not hot. Tom is sad. He sips a bit. "Not bad!" Tom grins. He sits on the log and sips from his pot.

Ron, a big cow, had a lot of fun on the farm. He got to hop and jog on a pop. Tom can hop so far! He ran to a pond and got on a log. The log was not on top of the mud. Tom fell off! What a lot of fun for Tom.

Short Vowel E

Ben met an pet in the red den. The pet can jet and zip. Ben fed the pet ten pegs of eggs. The pet has a den in the mud. Ben can see the pet bend and end. Ben has fun and he claps. The pet is glad and wags. Ben and the pet are pals. Ben and the pet nap in the sun.

Jen has a red hen. The hen pecks at the pen. Jen pets the hen and then, she lets it run. The hen pecks in the mud and then in the sun. Jen claps and grins. She feeds the hen. It is fun to see the hen run and jump. Jen and her hen play till the end of the day.

A bee met Ben in a den. Ben fed the bee, and the bee had ten sips of red jam. The bee set off, and Ben got a pen. Ben then jots, "A bee was in my den. It fed on jam. It was the best!" The bee hums and gets by Ben's leg. Ben is yet to let the bee get to the elk by the den.

Fred the deer met Ted. Ted had red fur. Ted and Fred fed on webs and stems. The men set nets, but Fred and Ted fled. They hid in the den. Ted then led Fred to a bed of wet mud. Fred felt glad to be safe. The end.

Ben and Ted set up a red jet. The jet met the bed. Ted let the jet zip. The jet sped up and up. Ben fed the jet. Ted and Ben bet the jet can get to ten. The jet hit ten! Ben and Ted get the win. They end the fun and pet the jet. Then, they rest.

Ken set the red egg on the bed. The egg fell and met a hen. The hen jutted, and the egg slid off. It hit the peg and then the pen. The egg did not yet break. It went to the edge. Ken got the egg. He put it back on the bed. Ken put the egg by Meg, his pet hen.

Ren the sheep met Jen on the red bed. Ren felt fed up. Jen had ten red pens. Ten and Jen set the pens on the bed. Jen bets Ren her pens can help. Ben pens a letter. Jen helps. Ren grins. Jen wins a new friend. Ren is glad he met Jen. Jen and Ren nap on the red bed.

Short Vowel U

Sun up. Bud runs up to a hut. A mud rug is on top. Bud tugs at the rug but it is snug. A bug hums in the hut. Bud hugs the jug and sips. A bun is on a cup. Bud has fun and sums up: "A hut is fun!" Sun sets. Bud jogs off. Hut in dusk.

The sun is up. It is fun to run in the sun. The sun is hot, but I am not. I sit on a rug and hug my pup. The sun is big and it can tug the fog up. The sun is up. We sip a cup. The sun can hum. We hum and hum.

A jug sat on a rug. It was a big jug, and it was red. A bug ran up to the jug and sat on it. The sun was hot, and the jug had mud on it. A cub ran by and hit the jug. The jug did not tip. The cub ran off. The bug sat on the jug in the sun.

A bug dug in mud and hum. It had fun but got in a rut. A pup dug it up. The bug ran to a jug. It hid in the jug. A kid saw the jug wig. The kid let the bug run. The bug dug in mud and hum. It had fun in the sun.

A bull runs up a mud rut. It is a big bull with a huff. The sun is hot, and the bull is in a rut. The bull rubs on a gum bud and huffs. It is a fun run for the bull. But, the mud is a bug. The bull tugs at a big tub. It is fun but hot.

A duck sat in mud by a hut. It dug in the mud with a tug. The sun was up, and bugs hum. The duck had fun and got a bug on its bun. It ran to a tub and got a rub. Then, the duck sat on a rug to nap in the sun. What fun!

A pup dug up mud. The pup had fun and ran in sun. A bug sat on a jug. The pup saw the bug and got up. The pup ran to the jug and hit it. The jug did tip. The bug ran off. The pup sat in mud, sad but snug.

Short Vowel I

Tim is in a big pit. It is dim in the pit. Tim digs in it with a tin bin. Tim sips a bit of his drink. Tim hits a big tin lid. It flips and fits in the bin. Tim grins and sits. Tim wins a pin! Tim zips his kit. Now, Tim can sit in the sun.

In a big pit, a pig digs in mud. It is Tim, a fat pig. Tim has a wig, and it is a hit! Tim can sit and sip. Tim can dip his wig in mud. Tim did fix his wig. Tim is fit and can zip! Now, Tim naps in his pit.

Liz had a big, red wig. It did not fit. It was a bit dim. It hid her lid. Liz sat in a pit and did fix it. The wig did fit at last! Liz did a jig with the wig. It was fun. Liz and the wig won!

Tim had six fish in his pit. It can zip in and out, and dig in mud. It is a bit dim but can hit a tin bin and not tip it. Tim can sit and grin as it flits. Tim's fish is not a fin. It is his kin.

Pim is a bird with a big tin bin. He sits in his bin and sips from his tin cup. It is full of mint mix. Pim sips and grins. He dips his fin in the mix and flits up. Pim sings as he spins in his bin. What fun Pim has with his tin!

Jim had a big kiwi. It was his top pick. Jim bit in. It was a hit! His kid, Sid, did not dig it. Sid hid his lip dip. Jim got Sid to try it. Sid did try. Sid did grin. Jim and Sid sat. Sid had a bit. Jim and Sid had fun.

Tim and Kim hit the big hill with a kit. In the kit is a red kite. Kim can fix the kite. Tim can flit it in the sky. The kite dips and zips up high. Tim and Kim sit and grin. The kite is fun! The kite can fly! Tim and Kim had a fit of joy with the kite.

Words ending in S

Tom has lots of pets. He has six rats, ten bats, and two dogs. The rats sit on mats and nibble on nuts. The bats hang from pegs and flap at bugs. The dogs run and jump and wag their tails. Tom's pets are his pals. He loves all his pets and hugs them lots.

The sky has lots of stars. Some are big and some are small. Jess sees a map that has dots and bars. The map tells us the age of the stars. Jess taps the bars and adds dots. She sees that old stars are less hot. Jess grins as she pens her tips on the map. Jess and her pals all clap.

Sam has five apes. The apes pass gas and the kids giggle. The apes nap on mats in the sun. Gus taps on pots and pans. The apes clap and hop to the taps. Jess gets the apes figs and nuts. The apes munch and fuss less. Jess pats the apes as the sun sets.

The trees toss nuts and bugs in gusts. The winds pass and the tall elms sway. The fir hugs moss. Pups dig in mud as cubs nap in dens. The sun sets. Bats flit in dusk. All is at rest in the woods.

In the hills, two lambs, Bess and Russ, miss their pals. Bess sobs as Russ rubs his legs. The sun sets, and Bess sits on moss. Russ hops and jogs to find pals. Bess hums and taps. Russ yells, "Pals!" Pals Bill and Tess run to Bess. Bess grins. All the lambs hug. Now, Bess and Russ grin as all pals sing songs.

Sam and Meg are best buds. Meg has six red hats. Sam has fun hats too. Meg's hats sit on pegs. Sam's hats sit in bins. Meg and Sam mix and fix the hats. They pass hats and grin. Meg's top hats are big hits. Sam's sun hats are tops. The pals swap hats as the sun sets.

Cass has lots of cups on her desk. She sips from mugs as she sits and rests. Cass has fun with sips of sods. She has two jugs and six tin cans. Her top pick is the red pop. Cass sips and sips till the sun sets. She hums as the fizz pops. Cass grins with her lips on her sips.

Consonant ff

Tim had a big puff as he ran to the cliff. He saw a puffin with a stiff wing. It was on a cliff and off it fell. Tim slid off and got it. He had to huff and puff to lift it. He was so puffed, but the puffin was all stiff. Tim got it back on top of the cliff, safe at last.

Bill, a big, gruff buff wolf, sniffed the air for a whiff of food. He saw a cliff and stiff moss. Bill took off in a puff and ran fast. At last, he found a small calf by the cliff. The calf was off to find soft grass. Bill left the calf and went to sniff out bugs and fish. Bill was full and off to his den.

A stiff cuff sat on a sill. A swift gust made it lift off and drop. As it fell, it hit a clump of soft moss. A girl saw the cuff and jogged to pick it up. With a sniff, she found it was not damp. She slid the cuff on her arm, fpeting the snug fit. Now, her shirt looked neat with its cuff in place.

Tom had a big, puffy puff. It was so soft and full! Tom and his mum took the puff to sit on at a cliff. As the sun set, Tom had a sniff. The air was crisp and fresh. "Mum, can we sit on the puff and puff on this cliff till the stars pop up?" Mum said, "Yes, we can sit and puff till dusk." They both sat and felt snug.

Jill the giraffe had a stiff neck one day. She felt off and sad, so she lay by a cliff. A soft puff of wind came, and with it, a fluff ball. It was a tiny buff bird. It sang a riff that made Jill sniff but then grin. The tune was a gift to lift her mood. Jill's neck felt less stiff as she stood tall and proud.

A calf named Ruff had fun in a huff. With a sniff and a snuff, Ruff dug the soft silt till he fell. Ruff felt glum and was off in a puff. Then, with a huff, he got up and ran to a cliff. From the top, Ruff saw a buff pup. The calf and pup met, and off they ran, full of guff. They had a lot of fun!

Jeff and his pals had a fun day off. They ran to a cliff to puff on a big huff of air. The wind was stiff, and the sun was soft. As they sat, a cuff slid off and fell. "I will miss my cuff," said Jeff with a sniff. His pals all gave him a hug. What a day it was!

Consonant ll

Bill has a ball. He and his pals toss it on the hill. A gull flaps its wings as it calls from a wall. Bill's ball slips and rolls down. His pal, Jill, runs to grab it. They all laugh and clap. Bill yells, "Toss it back!" Jill lobs the ball up. It falls in Bill's arms. All is fun on the hill.

Jill and Bill had a pPam to go to the mall. They took a bus and sat in the back. At the mall, Jill got a doll and Bill got a ball. They saw a tall man sell maps. Jill and Bill had fun. When the sun set, they ran to catch the last bus. At last, they sat and had a rest.

Bill is a tall man. He has a big hill by his Pamd. Bill can call his pals to come and walk up the hill. His dog, Bob, will run up fast. At the top, Bill and his pals will sit and talk. They can see all of the town from the top. It is a fun trip for all.

Bill the bull had a big bell. He fell in a well in the dell. It was all still and dull. Bill will yell and yell. Will Bill get well? Jess, a girl, will pull. With a full tug, Bill is up. Now, Bill is well and runs up the hill. Jess pats Bill and Bill is glad. Jess and Bill will nap in the sun.

Jill has a small doll. The doll is soft and has a pink frill. Jill will call her doll Bell. Bell sits on a hill in the grass. Jill will roll Bell in a red pram. As they stroll, Bell falls on a ball. Jill is sad, but Bell is still all in one. Bell will still sit with Jill on the hill.

Jimmy has a big bell. The bell will ring at noon. It is so loud, it will fill the hill with its toll. All the kids will stop to look. Jess will clap and Bill will yell with joy. The bell is still and then will toll one last time. The hill is calm again. The kids will miss the bell till next time.

Tom had a long staff. He took it up a hill to tap a bell. The bell was dull, so it fell off. Tom set the staff on a rock and sat with it. He had a nap and did not miss the bell. With a grin, Tom and his staff slid back down the hill.

Consonant ss and zz

Tim had a big buzz in his ears. A big, fat bug had just zoomed by. Tim had to buzz off fast to miss the bug. As Tim ran, his legs got a bit of fuzz on them from the tall grass. The sun was hot, but Tim had fun. He got to his spot and sat in the grass. The buzz was all gone. Tim was glad.

Ben had a big red bus. The bus had a big, big buzz. It went fuzz, buzz, fuzz as it ran. Ben and his pals got on the bus. It was a fun trip. The bus went past huts and hills. At last, the bus hit a mess of mud. It was stuck. Ben and his pals had to push and push. At last, the bus got out. They all had fun.

Mass has a big red ball. Mass will pass the ball to Jess. Jess will toss it back fast. Jess and Mass buzz and fuzz at a big bug. The bug will buzz off fast. Mass and Jess will miss the bug and fuss. Then, Mass and Jess will hug.

Tess had a red dress. It was a big mess. Tess ran to the shop to get a mop. With a dab, she got rid of the fuzz. Then she saw a big fuzz ball. Tess gave it a pat. It was a soft cat! Tess was glad. She fed it and had fun. The cat sat on her lap. Tess was at bliss.

Jess has a pet rat. Jess and her rat buzz past a fuzz on a red rug. Jess taps on a big box. The rat hops in the box and naps. Jess sits and sips a mug of hot tea. She rubs her rat as it naps. Jess is glad her rat is a fan of big naps in the box. Jess grins as her rat zips off.

Brass is a jazz band's best pick. The brass bell and drum add sass. Fans clap and tap. The band's jazz is a hit. Jess and Russ play well. The hall hums with pizzazz. Jess taps the drum as Russ blows his horn. The band is all grins. They win big at the gig. Brass jazz is tops!

Finn had a big, lush mass of grass. It was a hit with all. As Finn sat on the grass, a fuzz of bugs did zip by. This did not fit with his wish. Finn did not fuss. He got a big, stiff mat and sat on that. Now, Finn can sit in bliss and not miss his nap. The buzz of the fuzz is now just a hum.

TEACHER GRATITUDE

Write a letter to a teacher who has had a memorable impact on your educational journey so far.

_____

_____

_____

_____

_____

_____

_____

_____

_____

FREE RESOURCES

If you want free resources,

please email

buddingbrainsbooksllc@gmail.com

to get access to our free

giveaways and strategy guides.

Made in United States
North Haven, CT
03 November 2024

59786763R00043